KU-515-391

£6.25

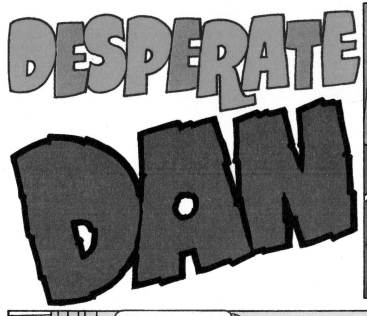

CUDDLES AND DIMPLES IN "SILLY SAYINGS" PART 1

BRASSNECK

Charley Brand has an amazing metal pal called Brassneck.

THAT'S ME, FOLKS.

Gordon Tait

MY FAVE BREAKFAST. CRUNCHY METAL NUTS WITH . . .

. . . SEMI-SKIMMED MOTOR OIL, YUM!

SIGH!

WHY THE SIGH, CHARLEY?

I'VE GOT TO HAND HOMEWORK IN TODAY . . .

. . . AND IT'S TOO HARD FOR ME TO DO.

LET ME PUT ON MY TEACHER HEAD, CHARLEY.

THEN I'LL BECOME CLEVER, LIKE A TEACHER.

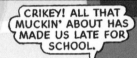

BLINKY

Later, in the bazaar . . .

I'LL TELL HIM WHAT TO DO WITH HIS DISGUSTING LESSONS.

THAT'S RIGHT! YOU TELL HIM, MUM.

At school —

OUT OF MY WAY, YOUNG MAN!

WAIT, MUM!

WHERE IS YOUR TEACHER, CHILDREN?

WHAT'S SHE DOING?

BEHIND YOU, MRS PAYNE!

WHY DO YOU WANT YOUR PUPILS TO BE DISGUSTING?

ER — I THINK YOU'VE GOT IT WRONG!

I SAID WE'D BE "DISCUSSING" THINGS THIS MORNING!

OOOH!

CORPORAL CLOTT

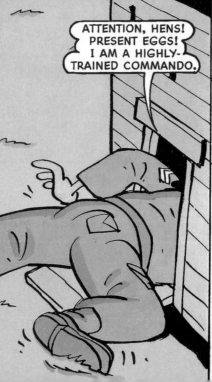

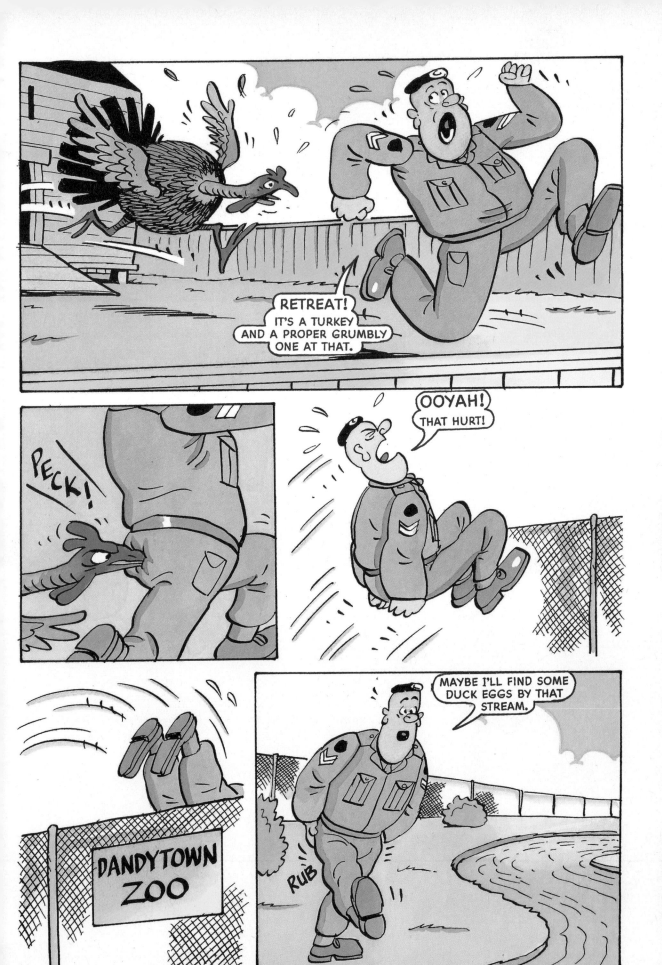

Did you find the hidden football? Turn the page for the answer, where you will find out exactly where it is.

the A to Z of being a PERIL

A for, ALLO, Folks!

B for BERYL'S BEST BEHAVIOUR –which you won't see here.

C for CATTYPULT –the favourite weapon of a Peril.

SWIP
TWANG
PING
PONG

SPLIP SPLAT

SPLOT

FLOT

AMMO

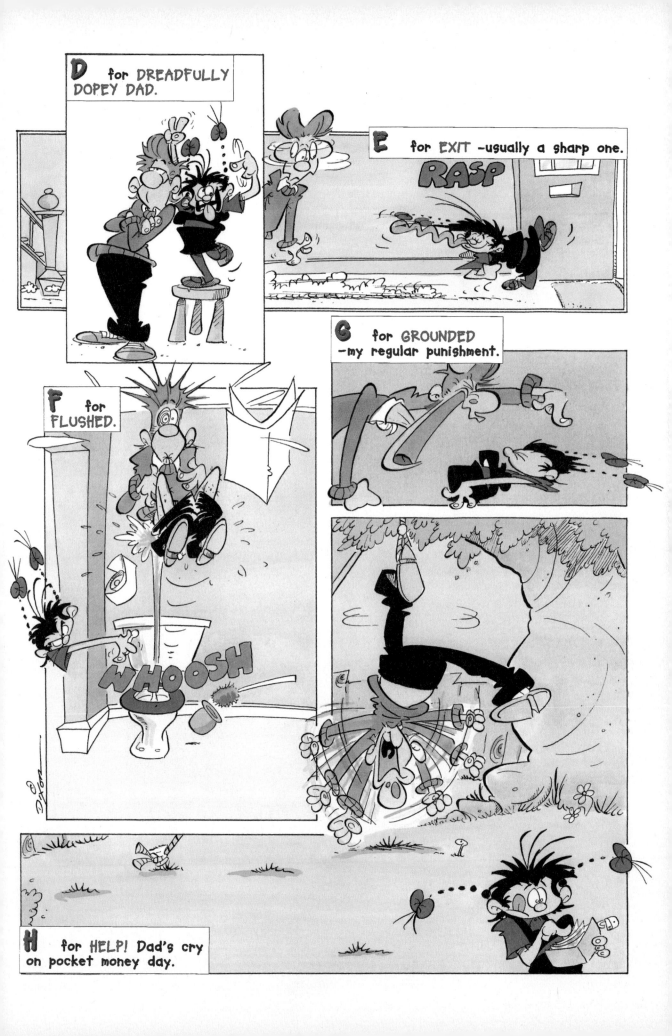

V for VIOLINS -and VIOLENCE!

W for WATER -as in, Water Bombs.

X for X-FILES -a fave way of scaring Dad.

Y more of soundalike. It's for Y ME?

SQUEAL!

Z for ZOO -which is where Dad thinks I really belong.

SNEAKER

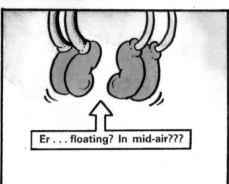

DAYS GONE BY

In World War II, the blitz — a series of air-raids on Britain by Germany — forced everyone to take cover in shelters and in the Underground system in London. The DANDY comic helped to keep morale high in those dark days — none more so than KORKY THE CAT and his crazy crew!

JAK and SPIKE

in DEADLY TOYS

M-MAKE A FOOL OUT OF YOUR POOR OL' DAD, WOULD YOU?

NOT USSES, DADDUMS . . .

. . . YOU CAN MANAGE THAT ALL BY YOURSELF.

CHEEKY PUPS!

SNIGGER!

Then —

OH, CAREFUL, DADDUMS . . .

EEK! SLIPPERY SKATES!

RRRIP!

. . . REMEMBER — A STITCH IN TIME SAVES . . .

BLUSH!

OH, GAWSH!

. . . BLUSHES!

I'M GETTIN' ANNOYED AND I'M GETTIN' UP!

OH-OH . . .

NOW I'M GETTIN' GOING!

. . . TIME FOR USSES TO GO ALSO, AS WELL.

SMASHER

P5

COME ALONG, CLASS. WE HAVE AN OUTING TODAY.

YEAH?

WHERE TO?

DANDY SCHOOL

Inside —

AND HERE WE ARE — DANDYTOWN CASTLE.

COOL.

THE CASTLE'S A BIT CREEPY, ISN'T IT? OH, YES.

THAT'S BECAUSE IT'S *HAUNTED*.

UH?

THERE'S THE GHOSTLY CLANK OF CHAINS.

CLANK! RATTLE!

WHINE.

AND THEN THERE'S THE ICY DRIP OF ICY, GHOSTLY WATER...

SQUEAL!

...FOLLOWED BY THE HORRIFIC CRY OF...

SPRING TERM

Spring lambs were fun.

So were the last snows of spring.

Spring meant flowers —and hay fever for Teach.

And the best kind of spring, a way of escaping from Teach.

SUMMER TERM

As usual, I was waaay cooler than Teach.

The best thing about summer term? That's when the summer holidays started!

The worst thing? Finding out I was on holiday at the same place as Teach.

By the way, you should always remember to use sun-block at the beach.

AUTUMN TERM

Falling leaves were great for hiding under when I was bunking off.

And Autumn winds were useful, too – for getting rid of rotten old tests.

There was plenty of rain, which was great for muddy, sliding tackles.

And I had great fun with conkers, too.

WINTER TERM

School books were useful after all – for keeping warm in winter.

And there was fun to be had at the annual school play.

Teach got very Christmassy – whether he wanted to or not.

And then we decorated the school – so much that we couldn't get to the doors.

PHEW!

WELL, THAT'S LAST YEAR DEALT WITH.

AND NEXT YEAR, WE CAN DO IT ALL AGAIN!

AGH!

DANDY 2003

TEACH? ER, TEACH? HELLO? TEACH?

GNNN!

TEACH?

ANOTHER YEAR WITH YOU, YOU HORRID, SNEAKY, UNDERHAND, WICKED, NAUGHTY, EVIL . . .

WOOAH! SOUNDS LIKE TEACH HAS MORE THAN FOUR TERMS FOR ME.

EDDIE POTTER at Strange Hill School

Eddie Potter is the only normal pupil at a very strange school.

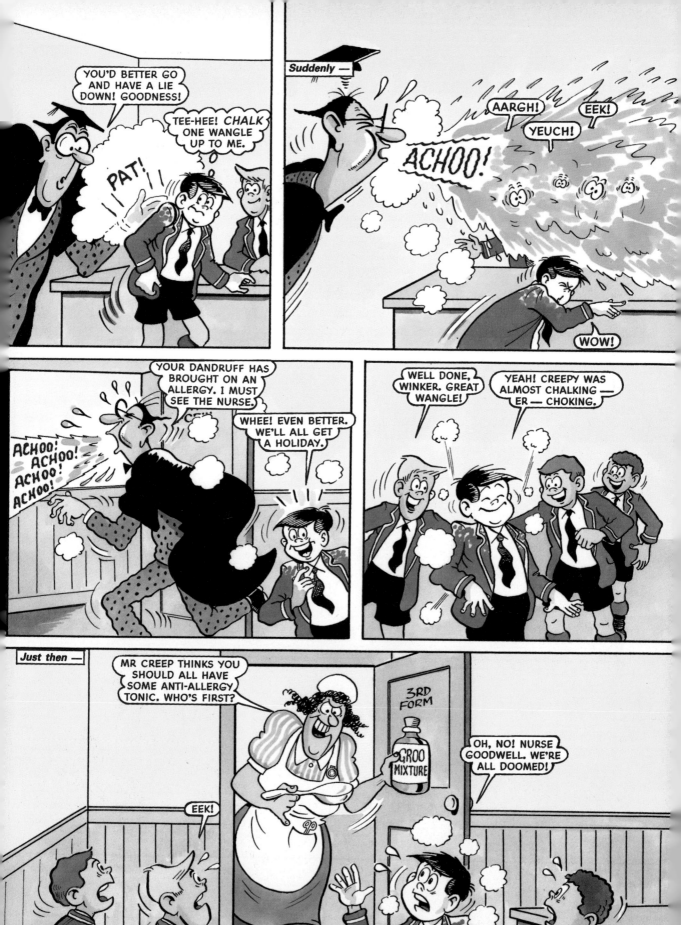

THE BANANA LUGHOLES DETECT MORE SNIVELLING.

IT'S CHIEFY. I HATE TO SEE THE BOYS IN BLUE BOO-HOO.

WEEP-WEEP!

IT'S AWFUL, BANANAMAN. TIGGY IS MISSING!

YOUR POLICE CAT?

I MISS HIM SOMETHING AWFUL.

HERE IS A NEWSFLASH THAT MAY HELP YOU, BANANAMAN.

EH?

THIS IS JACK THE KIPPER, CALLING BANANACHOPS.

I AM HOLDING THE CATS OF THE WORLD TO RANSOM. 10 THOUSAND POUNDS OR I MINCE THE MOGGY.

I REFUSE TO BE THREATENED BY A SMOKED FISH. I'LL HANDLE THE CASE, CHIEFY.

TIGGY IS RELYING ON YOU, MR B.

IT'S A CATASTROPHE. THE WHOLE CITY IS PUSSY-LESS.

WAIL!

SAVE OUR MOGGIES

WHERE'S MY CAT?

I WANT MY CAT

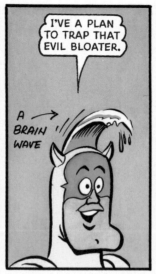

I'VE A PLAN TO TRAP THAT EVIL BLOATER.

A BRAIN WAVE

IT'S PURR-FECT.

JACK THE KIPPER WON'T BE ABLE TO RESIST ME.

MEE-OOW!

MEE-EE--OW!!!

SHADDUP, YOU BRUTE. I'M TRYING TO SLEEP.

WHIZZ!

PANG!

SHEESH! THIS CAT IS GETTING A DOG'S LIFE.

THROB!

PUSS-PUSS! NICE PUSSY.

THIS SOUNDS PROMISING.

OWEN GOAL

Dandy Town F.C. are 1-0 down with two minutes to go...

GO, OWEN.

I'VE BROKEN FREE OF THE DEFENCE.

NO, YOU HAVEN'T!

FOUL!

HOOF!

CLATTER

I AGREE! OOF!

I'M A-DA FREE KICK SPECIALIST.

DON'T CARE. I GOT FOULED. AND IT'S MY BALL SO I'M TAKING IT!

ZE BABY!

NIGEL PARKINSON

So...

I'LL SWERVE IT TO THE LEFT...

...OR MAYBE TO THE RIGHT.

NO! I'LL CHIP IT...

...OR BLAST IT!

But...

PHEEP!

WHAT? OH, BLAST IT, ALL RIGHT!

FULL-TIME!

WE WIN!

TWIT!

GRR! BUFFOON! YOU CAN TAKE AS MANY FREE KICKS AS YOU LIKE... FROM US!

HELP! I'M NOT THE BOOT BOY, Y'KNOW!

DAYS GONE BY

In 1953, Queen Elizabeth II was crowned. Her reign has lasted a very long time — but not as long as the DANDY'S, which is still comic royalty since the day it was launched on 4th December, 1937! KORKY THE CAT was in that first edition and, just as he celebrated the Queen's coronation, he's never 'flagged' since!

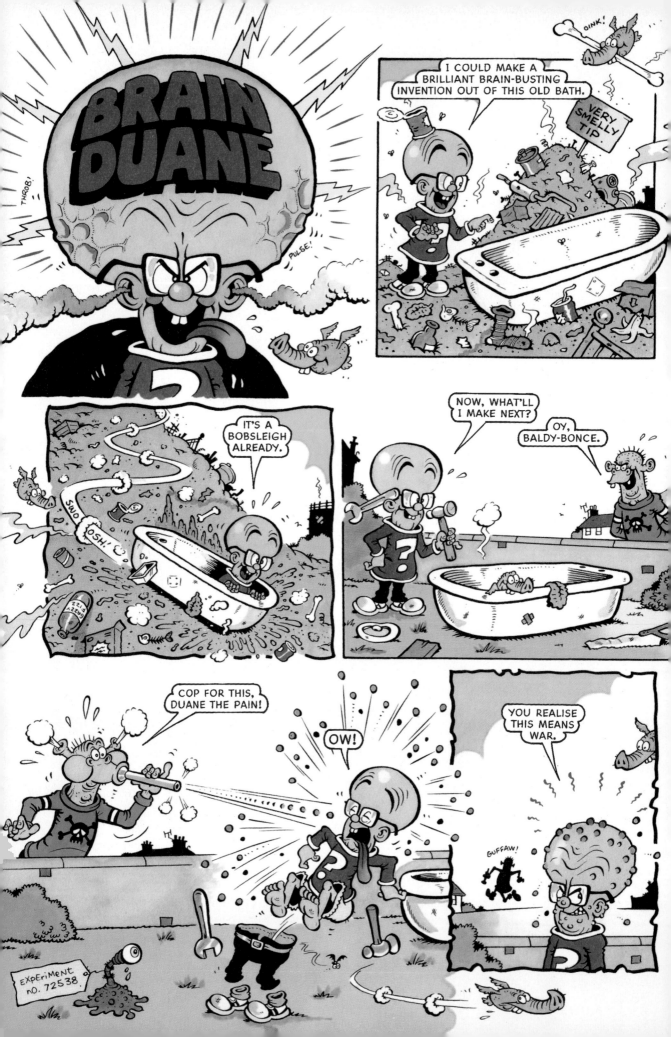

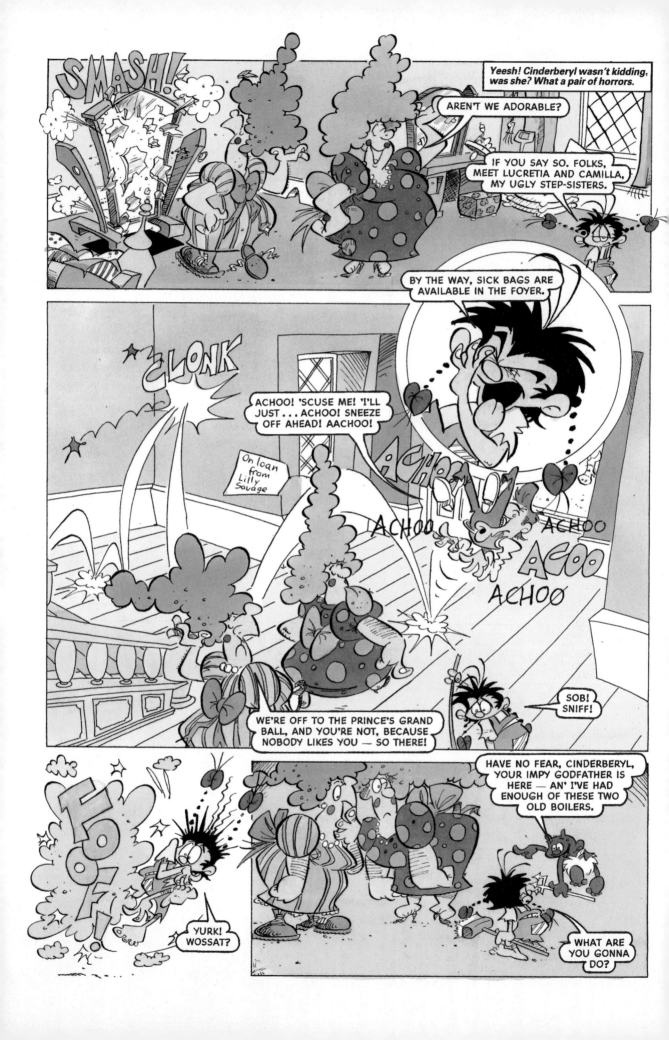

THIS CHAP'S THE KING OF THE JUNGLE— A COUSIN OF MINE, Y'KNOW!

PSST! BOW, YOU TWO! THIS IS THE KING!

WELCOME, SIRE!

Shortly . . .

WOULD YOU PULL MY CRACKER WITH ME, SIRE?

WHY, CERTAINLY, SMALL BOY.

HUH! WE GOT PAPER CROWNS IN OUR CRACKERS . . .

. . . BUT THE KING OF THE JUNGLE GETS A REAL CROWN IN HIS CRACKER!

AH, YES. A PERFECT FIT!

Soon after . . .

PLEASE LET ME SHOW YOU TO THE ROYAL BOX, O ILLUSTRIOUS COUSIN!

BOW!

ROYAL BOX? HOW SPLENDID!

Outside . . .

THIS WAY, SIRE!

BUT WHERE'S MY ROYAL BOX?

UP HERE! HEE-HEE!

PLONK!

DROP!

SLAP!

1ST CLASS TO AFRICA

BANG! BANG!

LET ME OUT, YOU REPUBLICANS!

I'M SURE HE WOULDN'T HAVE LIKED TO OVERSTAY HIS WELCOME!

BUT WHAT ABOUT YOUR CHRISTMAS DINNER? HE ATE THE LOT!

IT'S JUST AS WELL WE'VE GOT PLENTY AT OUR HOUSE, KORKY!

HA-HA! THAT'S SOLVED OUR KING-SIZED PROBLEM!

KORKY!

GROWING PAYNES

THE BOYS WILL BE HOME FROM SCHOOL SOON.

SIGH! THAT'LL BE THE PEACE SHATTERED I SUPPOSE.

NONSENSE! THEY'RE BOTH ON THEIR BEST BEHAVIOUR BECAUSE IT'S NEAR CHRISTMAS.

OH!

Suddenly —

PERCY! WHAT'S WRONG, BABY?

BAH! I HATE THEM! I WON'T DO IT!

HAVE YOU BEEN UPSETTING HIM, PETER?

NO, DAD! HE WAS LIKE THAT WHEN HE CAME OUT OF HIS CLASS.

TEACHER'S MAKING ME GO WITH THE GIRLS! SNIFF!

WHAT? OOH! THAT ISN'T FAIR!

THERE! THERE! I'LL TALK TO YOUR TEACHER TOMORROW AND SORT IT OUT.

SNIFF! THANKS! YOU'RE THE BEST MUM IN THE WHOLE WORLD.

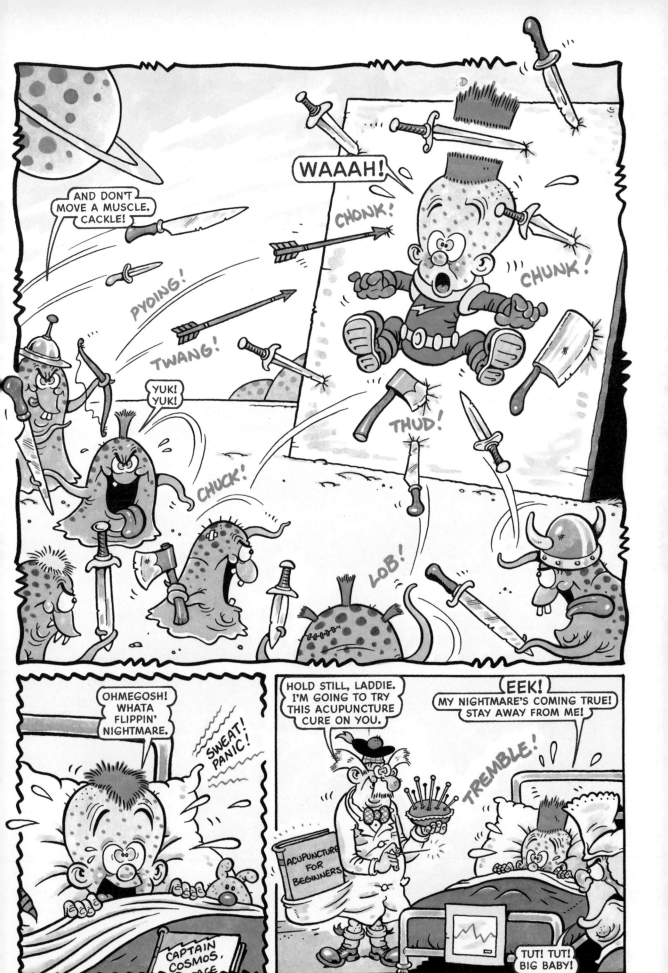

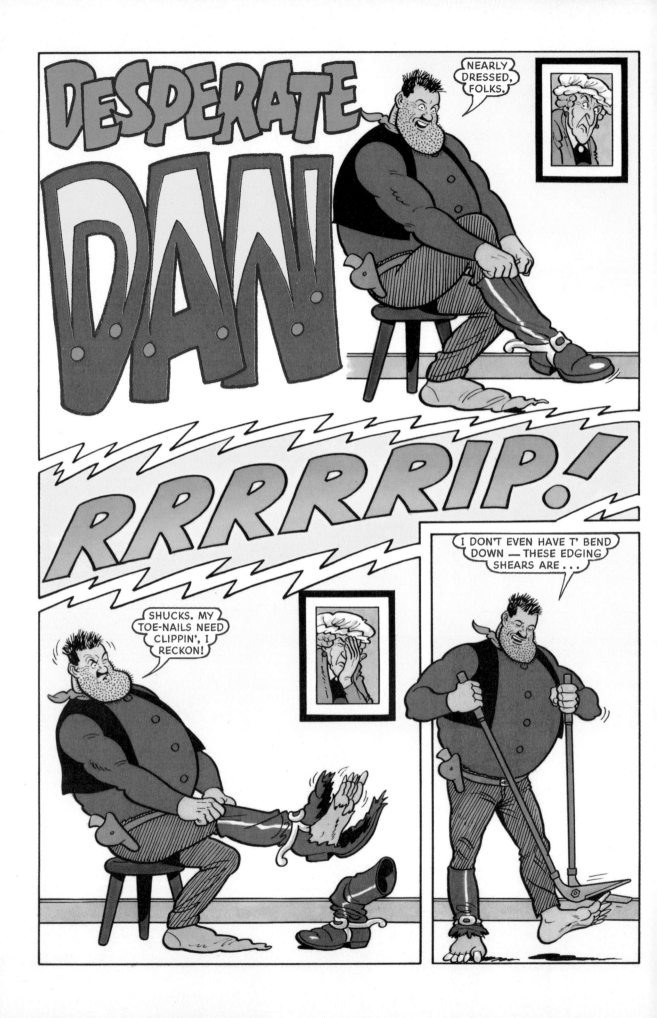

... BROKEN. THOSE NAILS SURE ARE TOUGH, LITTLE CRITTERS!

SMASH!

CLANK!

SNAP!

I'LL JUST HAVE TO FILE THEM DOWN.

HERE GOES!

RASP!

RASP!

MARVO

THE WONDERCHICKEN

and

Henry Thrapplewhacker 49th

MARVO'S BIG TOP TIGHTROPE WALK

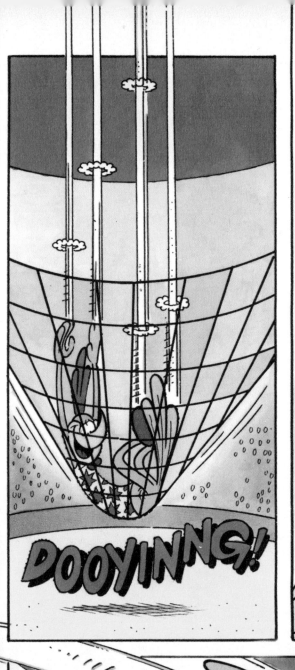

DOOYINNG!

BOYING!

AAARRRGH!!

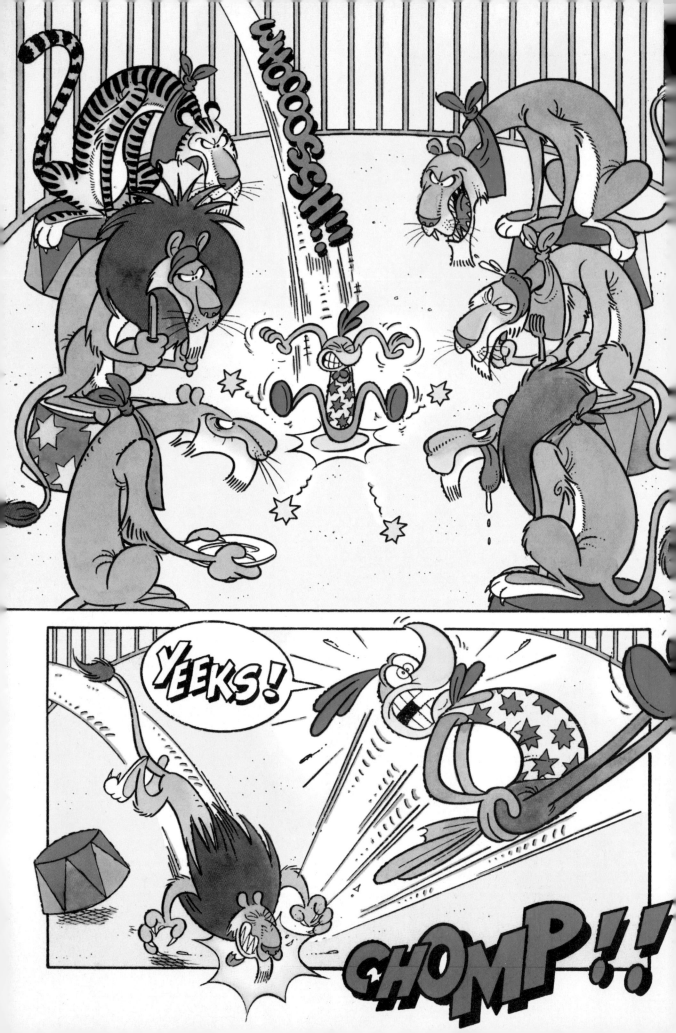

Well, pardners, here we are near the end of another DANDY book an' I'm sure you'll agree it's been a whole buncha rootin'-tootin' fun with a capital F! However, the fun doesn't have to stop here — you can catch up with your comic pals every week in the world-record-holdin' DANDY, so I hope y'all join us there!
'BYE!
Desperate Dan
XXX

DAYS GONE BY

Meet the original boy-band — The Beatles! From their first single in 1962 to their last in 1970, the fab four from Liverpool ruled the music world! But not only did they have a huge influence on music — they also influenced clothes and hairstyles — even in THE DANDY. Just look at BULLY BEEF — that's a Beatles-cut mop-top if ever we saw one!